This book is to be returned on or before
the last date stamp

PET

The Road to London

Stories linking with the History
National Curriculum.

First published in 1997 by Franklin Watts
96 Leonard Street, London EC2A 4RH

Text © Andrew Matthews 1997

Illustration © Stephen Lewis 1997

Editor: Matthew Parselle
Series editor: Paula Borton
Designer: Kirstie Billingham
Consultant: Dr Anne Millard

A CIP catalogue record for this book
is available from the British Library.

ISBN 0 7496 2609 7

Dewey Classification 942.083

Printed in Great Britain

The Road to London

by
Andrew Matthews
Illustrations by Stephen Lewis

W
FRANKLIN WATTS
NEW YORK • LONDON • SYDNEY

1

Clogger

Clogger was bursting for a pee. He could have asked Miss for permission to leave the room, but he hated using the school lavs. Everyone did, because they were smelly and even in summer they were cold. It wasn't summer now, but grey October.

Rain was falling outside and freezing draughts blew round Clogger's legs. He wished his place was nearer the gas fire, he wished the bell would ring so that he could go home – most of all he wished that he could have a pee.

Clogger had dark hair that Grandad had cut short at the back and sides with a pair of funny clippers. The clippers had two rows of teeth like a comb and when Grandad squeezed the handles together, the teeth moved sideways like a spider's jaws.

Clogger felt daft, sitting in a chair with a pudding basin over his head, but Grandad told him it looked like a soldier's helmet.

Clogger's eyes were brown and his nose was turned up at the end. His grey jumper had holes in the elbows and the seat of his shorts had been patched three times, each patch a different colour. His right sock was blue and was pulled up over his knee, the left one was brown and had slid down so that it looked baggy. The blue sock was an old one of Grandad's, the brown sock had been Dad's.

On his feet, Clogger wore the wooden-soled clogs that had given him his nickname.

He had made the name up himself, because it was better than his real name, Eustace.

Just before the end of school, Miss made the class tidy their things away. When the bell rang, the children put their hands together, chanted a prayer and then filed out out quietly, a row at a time. As soon as Clogger was in the school yard, he stuck his arms out straight. In his mind, they turned into metal wings and he became an aeroplane.

Clogger ran across the yard making the sound of the engine – "YEEE-OWW!" When he did his aeroplane running, he was faster than anything.

Clogger climbed over the iron railing at the side of the yard – he had been caned once for doing it, but this was an emergency – and dropped down onto a cinder path behind a row of houses. Clogger's clogs made a squeaky, squelchy sound as he ran through the sleet. At the end of the path a grassy slope led down onto a patch of waste ground. Clogger zoomed down the slope and crossed the road. Along the road nearly all the shops were boarded up. Clogger could just about remember when the shops had been open, but that had been before the Slump. Dad had once tried to explain about the Slump to Clogger, but Clogger had not really understood. He knew what the Slump meant, though – it meant men out of work and no wages coming in. It was the same all over Jarrow – shops shut up and men standing about, waiting for

something that never seemed to come.
Clogger's Dad was one of them. Every
morning he left the house as if he were off
to work, and spent the day hanging round
the streets, talking to his mates. Every
evening when he came in, Dad's eyes
looked sadder.

Clogger came to the top of his street. There was no time to go through the front of the house, so he dodged down the back alley. He rattled open the back door and bent down to look under the lav door to see if anyone was inside.

He was in luck – it was empty!

Mam was in the back parlour, darning a pair of socks. Grandad had the Family Bible open on the table and was reading from it, moving his lips and following the words with his finger. Penny the cat was a ginger pool in front of the range.

In the hearth, the fire burned blue and
green. Dad said it was because the coal had
been picked up from the beach and had salt
in it. Mam said she didn't care where the
coal came from, as long as it was cheap.

Mam looked up when Clogger came in.
Out of habit, she looked at the place on the
mantelpiece where the clock used to stand,
forgetting that Dad had taken the clock to
the pawn shop ages ago. "I wasn't
expecting you home yet!" Mam said.

"Did you leave school early?"

"No, fast," said Clogger.

"You'll meet yourself coming back, one day," grunted Grandad.

Clogger warmed himself by the fire. There was a saucepan bubbling next to the kettle on the hob.

"What's for tea, Mam?" Clogger asked.

"Ask no questions and you'll be told no lies!" said Grandad.

"Bread and gravy," Mam said. "I've got a heart for your Dad."

"So that's why you married him!" said Grandad. He laughed at his joke then picked up the teapot that was standing on the table and poured tea into a jam jar.

The tea looked red, and black leaves swirled
in it like rainclouds. Grandad took a swig
from the jam jar and smacked his gums.
"That's the stuff to give the troops!" he said.

Dad came in at five o' clock. He was so excited that he walked straight into the parlour without taking his cap or coat off. "You'll never guess what!" he said.

"You'll have to tell us then," said Mam. "Those beggars in London have let us down!" Dad said. "The Government won't do anything to help us. The President of the Board of Trade, that Walter Runciman said *Jarrow must work out its own salvation.* I read it in the paper, like."

"What does it mean, Dad?" asked Clogger.

Dad swept off his cap and shook rain from it. Some of the drops fell on Penny, who sat up and looked offended.

"It means we've got to save ourselves, bonny lad," said Dad. "And by God, we're going to!"

"Oh aye?" chuckled Grandad. "How are you going to do that, then?"

"We're going to march down to London," said Dad.

"What difference will that make?" Grandad said. "Folks in London don't care that for us!" He snapped his fingers.

"Well, we're going to make them care," said Dad. There was a proud look in his eyes, a look that Clogger hadn't seen since the shipyard closed.

2

Schemes

Next morning, in the school yard at playtime, Clogger was talking to two other children from his class, Amy Wetherall and Peter Clegg. He was telling them about what his Dad had said the night before.

"They've made a petition," he told them.

Peter sniffed and rubbed his runny nose on his sleeve. "What's a permission?" he said.

"Not a permission, a petition!" said Clogger. "It's like a letter to Mr Baldwin saying that he ought to help us. Over eleven thousand people have signed it to show they agree."

Peter, who had trouble with his seven times table, was impressed.

"Eleven thousand!" he gasped.

"Eleven thousand, five hundred and seventy-two," said Clogger.

Amy had been chewing the end of one of her plaits. She took it out of her mouth and said, "Who's Mr Baldwin? Is he the King?"

"He's the Prime Minister," Clogger explained. "He's the man who's running the country."

"Huh!" said Amy. "Well he's not running it very well, is he?"

"What's going to happen to this petition thing, like?" asked Peter, frowning so hard that his forehead crinkled up like a bowl of cold porridge.

"It's going to London," said Clogger.

"London's hundreds of miles away!" Amy said. "How's it going to get all the way down there?"

"They're going to put it in an oak box and carry it," said Clogger. "Two hundred men are going to march from Jarrow to London to give it to the Prime Minister."

"What if he's not at home?" said Peter.

Clogger ignored him, and said, "My Dad's going on the Crusade."

"Will he wear armour and ride a horse?" Peter said.

"Not that kind of Crusade, daftie!" said Clogger. "The march is going to be called the Jarrow Crusade. There'll be banners and a harmonica band – it'll be grand! Dad reckoned it would take four weeks to walk from here to London."

Peter's eyes went as round as footballs. "Four weeks?" he cried. "But that's..." He tried to work it out by counting on his fingers, but they got tangled up. "That's a really long time!" he said.

"Aye, but it'll be worth it!" said Clogger. "It's going to be in all the papers, and on the newsreel in the pictures as well.

Everybody in the country will know about it!"

"Your Dad's going to be on the films?" said Amy. "Will he be in one of those film star magazines?"

Clogger laughed at the idea. "I don't think so!" he said. "Mam said if anyone tried to take Dad's picture, his face would break the camera!"

In spite of his joke, Clogger was proud that his Dad was going to march in the Jarrow Crusade – and he was more than a bit jealous as well. The Crusade was going to be a great adventure, and Clogger had always wanted to have an adventure.

That evening, when Dad came in, he seemed more excited than ever. "It's going to start next Monday," he announced. "The appeal has raised eight hundred pounds!"

"Where from?" said Mam.

"All over," said Dad. "People have heard about what we're doing, and they've sent money to help us. We're going to use it to buy leather and nails to mend our boots when they wear out, and train tickets back from London."

Mam looked worried. "Where will you all sleep, pet? And what will you eat?"

"The National Unemployed Workers' Movement is taking care of all that," said Dad. "We're going to stop the night

in church halls and schools along the way, and there'll be a bit of supper for us as well."

Mam shook her head and wrinkled up her mouth, the way she always did when she was unhappy about something. "Well I don't know, I'm sure!" she said. "D'you think it's going to do any good?"

"It's better than standing round on the streets doing nothing," Dad said. "At least it'll show everybody how badly the men of Jarrow want to go back to work."

Grandad sighed. "By! If I were twenty years younger, I'd go with you!" he said.

"Well I'm younger," said Clogger.

Grandad, Mam and Dad all turned to look at him, and Penny, who was curled up on Mam's lap.

"What d'you mean, bonny lad?"
Dad said.

"I want to go on the Crusade too,"
said Clogger. "Can I, Dad?"

Grandad laughed, Mam smiled and
Dad came over to ruffle Clogger's hair.

"Your legs would
wear down to stumps!"
Dad said. "You stay here
and take care of Mam
and Grandad."

"Aw, Dad!" Clogger
grumbled.

"No!" Dad said sternly. "I've told you, you can't come with us, and that's that!"

Later on, when he was in bed, Clogger started thinking. "Dad said I can't go with the Crusade, but that's not the same as saying I can't follow behind, where he can't see me."

Clogger schemed himself to sleep.

3

The Crusade Begins

On Monday, October 5th, 1936, the Jarrow Marchers went to a special service at Christ Church. The men were dressed in their smartest clothes, and they all wore Crusade badges on the lapels of their jackets. The service was given by the Bishop of Jarrow and was attended by the Mayor, the Town Clerk, Miss Ellen Wilkinson MP and as many people as could be fitted into the church.

Outside a large crowd waited. Among the crowd were reporters, photographers

and a team of men making a newsreel.
Local children, who had been given the day
off school, ran about excitedly and were
told off by their parents. When the
Marchers came out of the church, there
was a loud cheer.

The Marchers set off down the long
road to London, led by Miss Wilkinson and
the Mayor, who were going to walk with
them all the way. Miss Wilkinson had her
dog with her, a black Labrador who pulled
on its lead as it walked along, showing its
big red tongue in a dog's grin. They passed
through streets lined with people who
waved and shouted encouragement.

Mam, Grandad and Clogger watched the
Marchers pass, and when Dad went by
they shouted louder
than anyone.
Dad was one
of the two men
holding up the
banner
with
'Jarrow
Crusade'
printed
on it. Clogger felt so proud
that shivers ran up and down his back.
Mam was crying, and Grandad had a tear
in his eye.

"It reminds me of the Great War,"
Grandad said. "All those brave lads who
marched off to fight in France and never
came back."

"Oh, don't say that!"
sobbed Mam.
"Don't fret, Mam!"
said Clogger.
"They'll be back."
After the last
of the Marchers had
disappeared around
a corner, the people
watching began to drift off.
"Come away now, our Eustace," said
Mam. "Let's go home."

"Aw, Mam!" said Clogger. "I wanted to go over to Peter Clegg's house. We're going to have a game of footy with some of the other lads from school."

Mam frowned, and for a moment Clogger was afraid that she was going to say no.

Then Grandad said, "Let the boy play! He's that excited, if you try and keep him in, he'll be hopping about like a flea on a dog's backside."

"All right then," Mam told Clogger. "But mind you're home for your tea."

Clogger put his hand behind his back and crossed his fingers so that he would not have bad luck from telling fibs. "I will be," he said, and

he was off, aeroplane running for all he
was worth.

As he ran, Clogger thought about the
note he had left on the bed he shared with
Grandad. He had written it with a pencil,
on an old piece of brown
wrapping paper.

Dear Mam & Grandad,
I have gone on the March
to London because I want to have an
adventure. Do not worry I will be
alright.
your loving
Clogger.

Instead of going
to Peter's house, Clogger ran to the cinder
path at the side of the school. Peter and
Amy were waiting for him, as they had
promised. Peter was holding the canvas
back-pack that contained Clogger's
supplies – two slices of bread that he had

secretly sliced off the loaf in the pantry,
an onion and an old lemonade bottle filled
with water.

"I scrounged an apple off my Auntie yesterday," said Peter. "I've put it in the bag for you."

"Thanks, you're a real pal!" said Clogger. "And I've brought this," said Amy. She handed Clogger three halfpennies. "That's all my savings," she said. "I was going to buy Mam and Dad a Christmas present, but this is more important than Christmas."

Clogger was so surprised that he did not know what to say. He thought about giving Amy a kiss on the cheek, but

decided that it would be too soppy and
shook her hand instead. "I'll pay you back
one day," he promised. He slipped his
arm through the strap
of the back-pack.
"Time I was off!" he said.

Clogger knew that the Marchers were
planning to spend the first night in Chester-
le-Street, which was miles and miles away.
He had no idea how long it would take to

walk there, but it would probably be hours and he decided to count his footsteps to pass the time. He had to give up after one hundred and fifty, because saying the numbers under his breath took longer than a step did and he got mixed up. Instead, he imagined what London was like. He knew it was even bigger than Newcastle upon Tyne, and that lots of famous people lived there.

Maybe, when he got there, the Prime
Minister would ask him
in for a cup of tea
and a piece of
bread and dripping...

It was dark when Clogger reached
Chester-le-Street. The lighters were out,
turning up the gas lamps with their long

poles. Clogger's legs ached. They felt
as heavy as lumps of lead and his feet
were sore.

He kept telling himself, "Just one more
step! Just one more step!" He was so tired
that his eyelids kept drooping, and his feet
would not go where he put them.

Clogger walked straight into someone.
The shock made him come wide awake.

He blinked his eyes and saw that he had
collided with a policeman.

"Mind where you're going, bonny lad!"
the policeman said.

"Sorry, constable,"
said Clogger. "Are
the men from Jarrow
here yet?"

"Why, aye!" the policeman said.
"They're in the Church Hall just down the
road, and —" He stopped and frowned

suspiciously at Clogger. "Just a minute, is your name Eustace Jessup?" he demanded.

"Yes," said Clogger.

The policeman put his hand on Clogger's shoulder. "I think you'd better come with me!" he said. "We've been looking for you!"

4

To London

Clogger's mouth fell open in astonishment. "Me?" he said. "How did you find out about me?"

"From your Mam," the policeman said. "As soon as she read your note, she went down to Jarrow police station and

47

showed it to the Sergeant. He rang our Sergeant, and we've been on the lookout for you all afternoon."

Clogger had never been in trouble with the police before. He imagined himself behind bars, with a ball and chain around his ankle and nothing but bread and water to eat and drink. "Will I have to go to prison?" he said nervously.

"Worse than that!" said the policeman. "You'll have to go straight to the Church Hall and see your Dad."

At the hall, some of the Marchers were eating their supper, others were having ointment put on their blisters. When Clogger and the policeman appeared, there was cheering and clapping. Dad came rushing over. First he gave Clogger a hug, then he gave him a telling off.

"What did you think you were playing at?" Dad said. "Your Mam and I have been that worried! It's off home with you first thing in the morning, my lad!"

Clogger was tired and hungry, Dad
was angry with him and everything had
gone wrong. Big tears started to roll down
his cheeks.

Then Clogger heard one of the
Marchers say to Dad, "Don't be so hard
on the boy, Tom! He's shown some spirit
coming all this way."

"Aye!" said another man. "After all,
it's our kids' future we're marching for! Let
him come with us if he wants to."

All round the hall there were nods and murmurs of agreement.

The policeman winked at Dad. "Looks like you're out-voted, Mr Jessup!" he said.

Dad frowned at Clogger, then his face softened into a grin. "All right, son," he said, "you're one of the Jarrow Crusaders now – though I shudder to think what your Mam's going to say to us both when we get home!"

There was another cheer, and Clogger went on crying because he was happy.

In the days that followed, there were times when Clogger was not so happy. It was fine to set off on a sunny morning, or to come to a large town where people greeted the Marchers like heroes – then it was like being on a sort of holiday. But out on the open road, miles from anywhere, trudging through cold, driving rain, Clogger sometimes wished that he had stayed at home. This adventure was nowhere near as exciting as he had expected – and it was hard work.

Five men became so exhausted that doctors ordered them home to Jarrow. The men's places were taken by relatives who had moved down South to find jobs, but the Marchers became worried and wondered who was going to drop out next. One night there was a rumour that Miss Wilkinson was too worn-out to carry on –

but Clogger's Dad didn't believe it. "She won't leave us!" he said. "She's a bonny little fighter, that one. She'll keep going until she drops!"

And he was right, because next morning Miss Wilkinson was at the head of the march, as usual. She looked pale and tired, but she refused to give up.

Day by day, bit by bit, the long road grew shorter, until at last the Crusade

reached London. When he reached the centre of the city, Clogger could hardly believe it. All the shops were open and their windows glittered like hoards of treasure. Prices were higher than the answers to the sums Clogger did at school. He could not understand how people in London could afford these things when people at home couldn't afford anything at all.

At one place, the Marchers passed a
group of young, well-dressed men
who were leaning against a long,
shiny car. They seemed angry.

"Boo! Bad show!"
one of them shouted.

"Get back to Jarrow,
where you belong!"
jeered another.

"What's up with them,
Dad?" Clogger asked.

"Ignore them!" said Dad. "They're afraid that folks like us want to take away what they've got."

"But we don't, do we?" said Clogger.

"No," said Dad. "All we want is a decent living."

For the last part of the march, the Jarrow Crusade was led by a brass band to Marble Arch. There were crowds, and

hundreds of policemen – some riding horses – and long speeches that Clogger did not understand. He also did not understand why Mr Baldwin refused to meet the Marchers after they had walked hundreds of miles to see him.

"He's frightened," Dad explained. "The whole Government's afraid that if they listen to us, there'll be a revolution, like the one they had in Russia."

"There won't be, will there, Dad?" said Clogger.

"Of course not!" Dad said with a laugh. "All we want is fair treatment, but I don't think Mr Baldwin sees things that way."

"But he will open the shipyard again, won't he?" said Clogger.

"I don't know, son," Dad said. "But whether he does or he doesn't, at least we can say we tried to get things changed. At least we've shown that the people of Jarrow haven't lost their fighting spirit."

The petition was delivered, there were more speeches and then it was over. The crowds went home, and so did the Marchers.

CLASS

On the train back to Jarrow, Clogger was quiet for a long time. He was trying to make sense of everything that had happened. "Dad," he said eventually, "isn't there a way of sharing things out, so that rich people aren't quite so rich, but people like us have got enough to get by?"

Dad sighed. "That's a difficult question, son," he said. "But someone's going to find an answer to it some day."

"Maybe I will!" said Clogger. "Maybe I'll grow up to be Prime Minister, and then I can get things changed."

Dad laughed. "I wouldn't be surprised, son," he said. "I wouldn't be surprised at all!"

Notes

Jarrow

Jarrow was once a prosperous town, part of the ship-building industry based by the River Tyne in the North-East of England. In Jarrow, the biggest employer was Palmer's Ship Yard. When Palmer's closed in the summer of 1934, more than seven out of every ten men in the town found themselves out of work, and there were no other jobs for them to do.

The Depression

During the 1930s, the whole world suffered from the 'Slump', or 'Depression' as it was also known. In Britain, there were 2 million people unemployed and the number rose. By 1936, things had begun to improve in some parts of the country, but Jarrow took longer than most to recover.

On the dole

Unemployed people could claim benefit – the 'dole' – but this was hardly enough to live on. In 1936, an unmarried man could claim 15 shillings (75 pence) a week, which was supposed to pay for his rent, heating, lighting, clothing and food. It was calculated at the time that an unmarried man needed 22 shillings 9 pence (£1.14) plus money for rent to meet his most basic needs.

The families of unemployed workers were sometimes forced to sell things for money, such as their furniture and even their best clothes. Poor families ate less meat, fresh vegetables and fruit and drank less milk. They ate more potatoes, bread and margarine – cheap food that 'filled them up' but was less healthy.

The Jarrow March

The Jarrow March was known as a 'hunger march' at the time. There were other hunger marches in Britain during the 1930s, but the Jarrow March was the most famous. Unfortunately it did not change the Government's policies and unemployment in Jarrow stayed high. However, the March did alert people in the Midlands and the South to the plight of the people in the North.

In 1939, three years after the Jarrow March, Britain declared war on Germany and World War Two began. Soon, the shipyards were re-opened to build warships, and life in Jarrow slowly improved.

2078